Analogies and Idioms

5–6

Written by
Linda Schwartz

Editor: Pam VanBlaricum
Illustrator: Jenny Campbell
Production: Acorn Studio Books
Cover Designer: Barbara Peterson
Art Director: Moonhee Pak
Project Director: Linda Schwartz

Table of Contents

Introduction

Each book in the *Power Practice*™ series contains dozens of ready-to-use activity pages to provide students with skill practice. Use the fun activities to supplement and enhance what you are already teaching in your classroom. Give an activity page to students as independent class work, or send the pages home as homework to reinforce skills taught in class. An answer key is provided for quick reference.

Analogies and Idioms is filled with challenging activities to help students improve their vocabulary and creative thinking skills. The book is divided into two main sections:

ANALOGIES

In this section, students learn how to understand and to write various kinds of analogies. These include

- synonyms
- tools and people who use them
- antonyms
- things and their uses
- homophones
- things that are usually associated
- members of a group
- singular and plural spellings of words
- parts of a whole
- animal offspring and animal groups
- rhyming words

This section concludes with students creating their own analogy exercises for classmates to complete. Word lists of synonyms, antonyms, and homophones are included.

IDIOMS

This section gives students matching exercises to help them better understand the meanings of common idioms in the English language.

 Ask students to illustrate three idioms on a separate sheet of white, unlined paper. They should write the meaning of each idiom next to their drawing. Here are some idioms students can illustrate (or ask them to choose their own):

- feet of clay
- butterflies in one's stomach
- wear one's heart on one's sleeve
- miss the boat
- hit the ceiling
- kick up one's heels
- hold your tongue
- walk on air

Use these ready-to-go activities to "recharge" skill review and give students the power to succeed!

What Is an Analogy?

An *analogy* is a relationship between one pair of words or terms that serves as the basis for the creation of another pair of words or terms. Analogies are usually written in the following form:

start : stop :: high : low   (start is to stop as high is to low)

Notice that a single colon (:) is used in place of the words *is to* in both pairs of words. A double colon (::) is used in place of the word *as*.

How to Complete an Analogy

To complete an analogy, read the first pair of words. Think about the relationship between them—are they synonyms? antonyms? homophones? rhyming words? parts of a whole?

Try this sample—true : false :: easy :

- **A.** simple
- **B.** shaky
- **C.** eager
- **D.** hard

In this example, the words *true* and *false* are antonyms. They have opposite meanings. Which word among the four lettered answer choices means the opposite of *easy*? The correct answer that completes the analogy is **D.** *hard*.

Practice completing these analogies.

1 open : close :: up :
- **A.** elevator
- **B.** near
- **C.** down
- **D.** tall

> If you answered **C.** *down*, you are correct because *up* and *down* are antonyms just like *open* and *close*.

2 flower : flour :: sail :
- **A.** boat
- **B.** sale
- **C.** pail
- **D.** mast

> If you answered **B.** *sale*, you are correct because *sail* and *sale* are homophones just like *flower* and *flour*.

3 fox : foxes :: woman :
- **A.** lady
- **B.** womans
- **C.** man
- **D.** women

> If you answered **D.** *women*, you are correct because *women* is the correct plural spelling of *woman*, just like *foxes* is the plural spelling of *fox*.

Analogies and Idioms • 5–6 © 2007 Creative Teaching Press

Synonym Analogies

An *analogy* is the relationship between one pair of words that serves as the basis for the creation of another pair of words. In each exercise below, the first two words are synonyms—words that have similar meanings. Find the word that *best* completes each analogy, and circle the letter in front of your word choice. Use a dictionary if you need help.

1 big : huge :: messy :
- A. dressy
- B. tidy
- C. sloppy
- D. noisy

2 ache : pain :: dense :
- A. open
- B. thick
- C. calm
- D. narrow

3 journey : trip :: throw :
- A. through
- B. plane
- C. sky
- D. toss

4 display : exhibit :: leave :
- A. arrive
- B. depart
- C. lessen
- D. believe

5 worth : value :: fright :
- A. night
- B. fabulous
- C. fear
- D. annoy

6 fix : adjust :: singe :
- A. single
- B. reap
- C. brag
- D. burn

7 rage : anger :: freedom :
- A. kingdom
- B. bargain
- C. liberty
- D. friend

8 misty : foggy :: empty :
- A. bland
- B. full
- C. lonely
- D. vacant

9 fierce : ferocious :: fair :
- A. fare
- B. reasonable
- C. uneven
- D. exact

10 opinion : view :: piece :
- A. peace
- B. entire
- C. part
- D. feast

Name _____ Date _____

More Synonym Analogies

An *analogy* is the relationship between one pair of words that serves as the basis for the creation of another pair of words. In each exercise below, the first two words are synonyms—words that have similar meanings. Find the word that *best* completes each analogy, and circle the letter in front of your word choice. Use a dictionary if you need help.

1 late : tardy :: small :
  A. large
  B. tiny
  C. hall
  D. insect

2 area : zone :: tight :
  A. wide
  B. fight
  C. snug
  D. loose

3 repair : mend :: simple :
  A. plain
  B. plane
  C. sky
  D. hazy

4 ill : sick :: enemy :
  A. war
  B. neighbor
  C. friend
  D. rival

5 teach : instruct :: copy :
  A. machine
  B. imitate
  C. reduce
  D. sloppy

6 useless : worthless :: govern :
  A. president
  B. government
  C. rule
  D. elect

7 pledge : promise :: excellent :
  A. fare
  B. superb
  C. unreasonable
  D. foolish

8 hurry : rush :: beg :
  A. leg
  B. instruct
  C. pleat
  D. plead

9 choice : option :: arouse :
  A. sleep
  B. awaken
  C. dream
  D. seek

10 gleam : shine :: genuine :
  A. real
  B. reel
  C. phony
  D. fake

Analogies and Idioms • 5–6 © 2007 Creative Teaching Press

Antonym Analogies

An *analogy* is the relationship between one pair of words that serves as the basis for the creation of another pair of words. In each exercise below, the first two words are antonyms—words with opposite meanings. Find the word that *best* completes each analogy, and circle the letter in front of your word choice. Use a dictionary if you need help.

1 above : below :: alike :
- **A.** unique
- **B.** similar
- **C.** different
- **D.** identical

2 good : evil :: on :
- **A.** go
- **B.** off
- **C.** of
- **D.** atop

3 save : spend :: rough :
- **A.** tough
- **B.** bumpy
- **C.** smooth
- **D.** sharp

4 down : up :: before :
- **A.** after
- **B.** noon
- **C.** earlier
- **D.** previous

5 fancy : plain :: remember :
- **A.** recall
- **B.** investigate
- **C.** forget
- **D.** recognize

6 believe : doubt :: crooked :
- **A.** irregular
- **B.** thief
- **C.** narrow
- **D.** straight

7 victory : defeat :: arrival :
- **A.** vacation
- **B.** attendance
- **C.** departure
- **D.** rival

8 comply : resist :: cheerful :
- **A.** ecstatic
- **B.** somber
- **C.** excited
- **D.** happy

9 omit : include :: exact :
- **A.** vague
- **B.** vogue
- **C.** identical
- **D.** precise

10 active : passive :: exterior :
- **A.** outside
- **B.** extraneous
- **C.** interior
- **D.** overabundance

Synonym and Antonym Analogies

An *analogy* is the relationship between one pair of words that serves as the basis for the creation of another pair of words. In each exercise below, decide if the first pair of words is a pair of synonyms or antonyms. Find the word that *best* completes each analogy, and circle the letter in front of your word choice. Use a dictionary if you need help.

1 minimum : maximum :: beneficial :
   - **A.** helpful
   - **B.** kind
   - **C.** temporary
   - **D.** harmful

2 drab : bright :: allow :
   - **A.** forbid
   - **B.** grant
   - **C.** tempt
   - **D.** pursue

3 identical : alike :: nimble :
   - **A.** thimble
   - **B.** rigid
   - **C.** spry
   - **D.** sluggish

4 grief : joy :: advance :
   - **A.** advantage
   - **B.** retreat
   - **C.** move
   - **D.** investigate

5 hardy : strong :: alone :
   - **A.** many
   - **B.** along
   - **C.** solitary
   - **D.** multiple

6 inferior : superior :: ambitious :
   - **A.** lazy
   - **B.** excited
   - **C.** dynamic
   - **D.** lucky

7 fearless : brave :: peculiar :
   - **A.** fussy
   - **B.** familiar
   - **C.** odd
   - **D.** normal

8 persuade : coax :: rough :
   - **A.** tight
   - **B.** coarse
   - **C.** smooth
   - **D.** silly

9 worst : best :: shrink :
   - **A.** think
   - **B.** swell
   - **C.** reduce
   - **D.** wrinkle

10 ordinary : normal :: divulge :
   - **A.** digest
   - **B.** disappear
   - **C.** disclose
   - **D.** desire

Analogies and Idioms • 5–6 © 2007 Creative Teaching Press

Noun Analogies

An *analogy* is the relationship between one pair of words that serves as the basis for the creation of another pair of words. Read the nouns in each exercise below, find the word that *best* completes each analogy, and circle the letter in front of your word choice. Use a dictionary if you need help.

1 salmon : fish :: beetle :
- **A.** ladybug
- **B.** insect
- **C.** needle
- **D.** reptile

2 toe : foot :: finger :
- **A.** nail
- **B.** ring
- **C.** hand
- **D.** elbow

3 toucan : bird :: daisy :
- **A.** tulip
- **B.** tree
- **C.** hazy
- **D.** flower

4 leaf : tree :: tire :
- **A.** rubber
- **B.** circle
- **C.** automobile
- **D.** boat

5 peanut butter : jelly :: bacon :
- **A.** pork
- **B.** crackers
- **C.** fish
- **D.** eggs

6 trumpet : instrument :: sandal :
- **A.** shoe
- **B.** heel
- **C.** belt
- **D.** leather

7 scale : fish :: feather :
- **A.** bird
- **B.** tickle
- **C.** light
- **D.** nest

8 broccoli : vegetable :: apricot :
- **A.** orange
- **B.** dessert
- **C.** bush
- **D.** fruit

9 coyote : mammal :: lizard :
- **A.** snake
- **B.** reptile
- **C.** desert
- **D.** bird

10 femur : leg :: scapula :
- **A.** spine
- **B.** skull
- **C.** shoulder blade
- **D.** arm

Name _____ Date _____

Verb Analogies

An *analogy* is the relationship between one pair of words that serves as the basis for the creation of another pair of words. Read the verbs in each exercise below, find the word that *best* completes each analogy, and circle the letter in front of your word choice. Use a dictionary if you need help.

1 trim : cut :: drop :
- **A.** droop
- **B.** extend
- **C.** fall
- **D.** climb

2 come : arrive :: scoop :
- **A.** dig
- **B.** sand
- **C.** snoop
- **D.** bury

3 vanish : appear :: increase :
- **A.** add
- **B.** decrease
- **C.** inquire
- **D.** include

4 taunt : tease :: shiver :
- **A.** divert
- **B.** deliver
- **C.** stiffen
- **D.** shake

5 inquire : ask :: choose :
- **A.** chase
- **B.** select
- **C.** waste
- **D.** repeat

6 answer : reply :: warn :
- **A.** caution
- **B.** discuss
- **C.** ignore
- **D.** mend

7 pout : sulk :: smother :
- **A.** bother
- **B.** breathe
- **C.** suffocate
- **D.** ignite

8 happen : occur :: bargain :
- **A.** pry
- **B.** negotiate
- **C.** begin
- **D.** invest

9 reject : accept :: fail :
- **A.** lose
- **B.** defeat
- **C.** succeed
- **D.** quail

10 defend : attack :: believe :
- **A.** listen
- **B.** betray
- **C.** accept
- **D.** doubt

Analogies and Idioms • 5–6 © 2007 Creative Teaching Press

Name _____ Date _____

Adjective Analogies

An *analogy* is the relationship between one pair of words that serves as the basis for the creation of another pair of words. Read the adjectives in each exercise below, find the word that *best* completes each analogy, and circle the letter in front of your word choice. Use a dictionary if you need help.

1 sad : jolly :: silly :
    A. nasty
    B. hilly
    C. frivolous
    D. serious

2 polite : rude :: flimsy :
    A. sturdy
    B. fancy
    C. loose
    D. insincere

3 candid : truthful :: ordinary :
    A. mean
    B. common
    C. unique
    D. odd

4 harmless : toxic :: foolish :
    A. ridiculous
    B. faulty
    C. fancy
    D. wise

5 enormous : huge :: apparent :
    A. accurate
    B. obvious
    C. oblivious
    D. obsolete

6 calm : serene :: precise :
    A. confusing
    B. precious
    C. exact
    D. showy

7 casual : formal :: deep :
    A. shallow
    B. complex
    C. dense
    D. creepy

8 timid : shy :: sincere :
    A. sensible
    B. prosperous
    C. faithful
    D. honest

9 common : rare :: fresh :
    A. fragrant
    B. rude
    C. stale
    D. clean

10 wild : tame :: simple :
    A. easy
    B. difficult
    C. plain
    D. stupid

Name _____ Date _____

Adverb Analogies

An *analogy* is the relationship between one pair of words that serves as the basis for the creation of another pair of words. Read the adverbs in each exercise below, find the word that *best* completes each analogy, and circle the letter in front of your word choice. Use a dictionary if you need help.

1 upstairs : downstairs :: loudly :
- **A.** noisily
- **B.** quietly
- **C.** carefully
- **D.** lavishly

2 slowly : hastily :: outwardly :
- **A.** merely
- **B.** jointly
- **C.** visibly
- **D.** inwardly

3 crazily : sanely :: calmly :
- **A.** cleanly
- **B.** nervously
- **C.** peacefully
- **D.** joyously

4 completely : thoroughly :: exactly :
- **A.** immediately
- **B.** orderly
- **C.** keenly
- **D.** precisely

5 prominently : noticeably :: harshly :
- **A.** severely
- **B.** finely
- **C.** humbly
- **D.** quickly

6 sincerely : insincerely :: passively :
- **A.** convincingly
- **B.** skillfully
- **C.** actively
- **D.** resentfully

7 intentionally : purposely :: fondly :
- **A.** hatefully
- **B.** openly
- **C.** plainly
- **D.** affectionately

8 clumsily : daintily :: legally :
- **A.** lawfully
- **B.** casually
- **C.** illegally
- **D.** usually

9 sensibly : wisely :: partly :
- **A.** wholly
- **B.** partially
- **C.** finely
- **D.** completely

10 shyly : meekly :: abruptly :
- **A.** suddenly
- **B.** angrily
- **C.** gradually
- **D.** perfectly

Analogies and Idioms • 5–6 © 2007 Creative Teaching Press

Food Analogies

An *analogy* is the relationship between one pair of words that serves as the basis for the creation of another pair of words. In each exercise below, find the relationship between the first pair of words. Then find the word that *best* completes the analogy, and circle the letter in front of your word choice. Use a dictionary if you need help.

1 cheese : milk :: ketchup :
- **A.** tomato
- **B.** hamburger
- **C.** relish
- **D.** apple

2 mousse : moose :: mussel :
- **A.** fish
- **B.** ocean
- **C.** muscle
- **D.** clam

3 whip : beat :: cut :
- **A.** fry
- **B.** chop
- **C.** steam
- **D.** knife

4 salt : pepper :: spaghetti :
- **A.** food
- **B.** noodle
- **C.** fork
- **D.** meatballs

5 raw : cooked :: tender :
- **A.** tough
- **B.** fender
- **C.** tasty
- **D.** soft

6 lemon : sour :: candy :
- **A.** dessert
- **B.** sweet
- **C.** chocolate
- **D.** licorice

7 tea : beverage :: cinnamon :
- **A.** orange
- **B.** bread
- **C.** oregano
- **D.** spice

8 cow : beef :: chicken :
- **A.** poultry
- **B.** hen
- **C.** turkey
- **D.** salad

9 mango : fruit :: turnip :
- **A.** carrot
- **B.** kale
- **C.** vegetable
- **D.** fish

10 steak : stake :: leak :
- **A.** water
- **B.** peak
- **C.** faucet
- **D.** leek

Name _____ Date _____

Sports Analogies

An *analogy* is the relationship between one pair of words that serves as the basis for the creation of another pair of words. In each exercise below, find the relationship between the first pair of words. Then find the word that *best* completes the analogy, and circle the letter in front of your word choice. Use a dictionary if you need help.

1 strike : bowling :: goal :
- **A.** basketball
- **B.** tennis
- **C.** hockey
- **D.** badminton

2 badminton : racket :: golf :
- **A.** birdie
- **B.** gulf
- **C.** tee
- **D.** club

3 boxing : ring :: tennis :
- **A.** court
- **B.** racket
- **C.** net
- **D.** field

4 baseball : sport :: chess :
- **A.** knight
- **B.** board
- **C.** game
- **D.** castle

5 offense : defense :: professional :
- **A.** professor
- **B.** parade
- **C.** amateur
- **D.** athlete

6 punt : football :: serve :
- **A.** skating
- **B.** baseball
- **C.** nerve
- **D.** volleyball

7 shoot : chute :: pedal :
- **A.** bicycle
- **B.** peddle
- **C.** medal
- **D.** foot

8 umpire : baseball :: referee :
- **A.** wrestling
- **B.** coach
- **C.** examine
- **D.** teacher

9 win : lose :: defend :
- **A.** protect
- **B.** attack
- **C.** depend
- **D.** football

10 course : coarse :: team :
- **A.** teem
- **B.** squad
- **C.** players
- **D.** ream

Analogies and Idioms · 5–6 © 2007 Creative Teaching Press

Number and Measurement Analogies

An *analogy* is the relationship between one pair of words that serves as the basis for the creation of another pair of words. In each exercise below, find the relationship between the first pair of words. Then find the word that *best* completes the analogy, and circle the letter in front of your word choice. Use a dictionary if you need help.

1 weighed : wade :: four :
- **A.** number
- **B.** for
- **C.** door
- **D.** double

2 scale : weight :: thermometer :
- **A.** depth
- **B.** time
- **C.** temperature
- **D.** weather

3 pint : quart :: pound :
- **A.** found
- **B.** yard
- **C.** inch
- **D.** ton

4 pentagon : five :: triangle :
- **A.** six
- **B.** three
- **C.** square
- **D.** rectangle

5 minuend : subtraction :: numerator :
- **A.** number
- **B.** division
- **C.** fraction
- **D.** multiplication

6 fathom : depth :: barometer :
- **A.** pressure
- **B.** balance
- **C.** volume
- **D.** capacity

7 factor : multiplication :: divisor :
- **A.** addition
- **B.** division
- **C.** advisor
- **D.** decimal

8 second : minute :: year :
- **A.** century
- **B.** fear
- **C.** month
- **D.** yard

9 fourth : forth :: cent :
- **A.** penny
- **B.** coin
- **C.** scent
- **D.** dollar

10 angle : protractor :: circle :
- **A.** ball
- **B.** round
- **C.** ruler
- **D.** compass

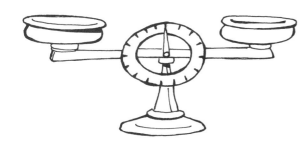

Name _____ Date _____

Animal Analogies

An *analogy* is the relationship between one pair of words that serves as the basis for the creation of another pair of words. In each exercise below, find the relationship between the first pair of words. Then find the word that *best* completes the analogy, and circle the letter in front of your word choice. Use a dictionary if you need help.

1 moo : cow :: bleat :
- **A.** sheep
- **B.** horse
- **C.** tiger
- **D.** cow

2 fox : foxes :: moose :
- **A.** deer
- **B.** meese
- **C.** moose
- **D.** mooses

3 tusk : elephant :: antler :
- **A.** horn
- **B.** horse
- **C.** zebra
- **D.** elk

4 cobra : reptile :: gerbil :
- **A.** fish
- **B.** insect
- **C.** hamster
- **D.** mammal

5 ornithology : birds :: zoology :
- **A.** plants
- **B.** animals
- **C.** biology
- **D.** insects

6 antenna : insect :: beak :
- **A.** leak
- **B.** bill
- **C.** bird
- **D.** snake

7 pride : lion :: pod :
- **A.** whale
- **B.** kitten
- **C.** sod
- **D.** rabbit

8 cat : feline :: dog :
- **A.** pet
- **B.** hog
- **C.** beagle
- **D.** canine

9 gosling : goose :: calf :
- **A.** antelope
- **B.** ostrich
- **C.** beaver
- **D.** giraffe

10 stork : bird :: sloth :
- **A.** reptile
- **B.** mammal
- **C.** fish
- **D.** cloth

Analogies and Idioms • 5–6 © 2007 Creative Teaching Press

Analogy Challenge #1

An *analogy* is the relationship between one pair of words that serves as the basis for the creation of another pair of words. In each exercise below, find the relationship between the first pair of words. Then find the word that *best* completes the analogy, and circle the letter in front of your word choice. Use a dictionary if you need help.

1 fawn : deer :: lamb :
- **A.** tiger
- **B.** sheep
- **C.** lion
- **D.** horse

2 gate : gait :: flower :
- **A.** petal
- **B.** daisy
- **C.** vase
- **D.** flour

3 wolf : pack :: cattle :
- **A.** herd
- **B.** cow
- **C.** ranch
- **D.** steak

4 duet : two :: quartet :
- **A.** music
- **B.** two
- **C.** instrument
- **D.** four

5 hidden : concealed :: murky :
- **A.** jerky
- **B.** dark
- **C.** clear
- **D.** concise

6 radius : circle :: spoke :
- **A.** wheel
- **B.** talked
- **C.** boat
- **D.** joke

7 glove : hand :: boot :
- **A.** shoe
- **B.** heel
- **C.** foot
- **D.** knee

8 sound : ear :: odor :
- **A.** smell
- **B.** lips
- **C.** eyes
- **D.** nose

9 plant : terrarium :: fish :
- **A.** salmon
- **B.** fin
- **C.** shark
- **D.** aquarium

10 inch : yard :: centimeter :
- **A.** liter
- **B.** mile
- **C.** meter
- **D.** circle

Analogy Challenge #2

An *analogy* is the relationship between one pair of words that serves as the basis for the creation of another pair of words. In each exercise below, find the relationship between the first pair of words. Then find the word that *best* completes the analogy, and circle the letter in front of your word choice. Use a dictionary if you need help.

1 minute : hour :: month :
- **A.** second
- **B.** calendar
- **C.** year
- **D.** April

2 Earth : planet :: sun :
- **A.** star
- **B.** moon
- **C.** round
- **D.** orbit

3 funny : runny :: paper :
- **A.** pen
- **B.** canvas
- **C.** notebook
- **D.** caper

4 pear : fruit :: carrot :
- **A.** cauliflower
- **B.** vegetable
- **C.** orange
- **D.** vitamin

5 cub : bear :: kid :
- **A.** goat
- **B.** shoat
- **C.** foal
- **D.** calf

6 caution : warn :: vanish :
- **A.** appear
- **B.** varnish
- **C.** disappear
- **D.** approach

7 weighed : wade :: metal :
- **A.** ore
- **B.** steel
- **C.** iron
- **D.** mettle

8 porpoise : ocean :: coyote :
- **A.** dessert
- **B.** desert
- **C.** wolf
- **D.** mammal

9 bed : sleep :: chair :
- **A.** sit
- **B.** couch
- **C.** hair
- **D.** footrest

10 clothes : hamper :: water :
- **A.** milk
- **B.** ocean
- **C.** glass
- **D.** liquid

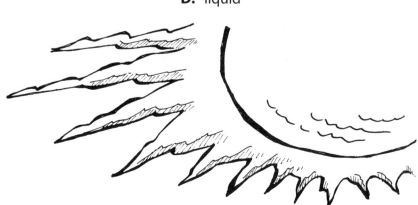

Analogies and Idioms • 5–6 © 2007 Creative Teaching Press

Analogy Challenge #3

An *analogy* is the relationship between one pair of words that serves as the basis for the creation of another pair of words. In each exercise below, find the relationship between the first pair of words. Then find the word that *best* completes the analogy, and circle the letter in front of your word choice. Use a dictionary if you need help.

1 scramble : egg :: knead :
- **A.** kneed
- **B.** need
- **C.** leather
- **D.** dough

2 strings : violin :: keys :
- **A.** piano
- **B.** house
- **C.** peas
- **D.** ring

3 sound : decibel :: electricity :
- **A.** static
- **B.** volt
- **C.** plug
- **D.** energy

4 maple : staple :: mellow :
- **A.** unruly
- **B.** mild
- **C.** pillow
- **D.** fellow

5 jacket : coat :: pennant :
- **A.** jewelry
- **B.** pole
- **C.** promise
- **D.** flag

6 woman : women :: child :
- **A.** toddler
- **B.** childs
- **C.** children
- **D.** childes

7 rooster : hen :: gander :
- **A.** bird
- **B.** goose
- **C.** farm
- **D.** geese

8 singe : burn :: gather :
- **A.** assemble
- **B.** rather
- **C.** disperse
- **D.** confuse

9 ruby : red :: lavender :
- **A.** green
- **B.** purple
- **C.** yellow
- **D.** white

10 stunt : trick :: feat :
- **A.** feet
- **B.** shoe
- **C.** deed
- **D.** fault

Name _____ Date _____

Analogy Challenge #4

An *analogy* is the relationship between one pair of words that serves as the basis for the creation of another pair of words. In each exercise below, find the relationship between the first pair of words. Then find the word that *best* completes the analogy, and circle the letter in front of your word choice. Use a dictionary if you need help.

1 club : golf :: racket :
   A. noise
   B. tennis
   C. packet
   D. ball

2 rake : gardener :: wrench :
   A. pipe
   B. tool
   C. painter
   D. plumber

3 knight : night :: isle :
   A. island
   B. sand
   C. vacation
   D. aisle

4 praise : humiliate :: magnify :
   A. enlarge
   B. experiment
   C. reduce
   D. expand

5 jealous : envious :: haughty :
   A. arrogant
   B. shy
   C. helpless
   D. hungry

6 hive : bees :: colony :
   A. cats
   B. spiders
   C. settlement
   D. termites

7 ostrich : chick :: kangaroo :
   A. joey
   B. pouch
   C. cub
   D. kit

8 pack : wolves :: gaggle :
   A. sheep
   B. cats
   C. bears
   D. geese

9 innocent : guilty :: permanent :
   A. hair
   B. lasting
   C. temporary
   D. forever

10 refuse : decline :: opinion :
   A. view
   B. freedom
   C. promise
   D. sorrow

Analogies and Idioms • 5–6 © 2007 Creative Teaching Press

Name _____   Date _____

Analogy Challenge #5

An *analogy* is the relationship between one pair of words that serves as the basis for the creation of another pair of words. In each exercise below, find the relationship between the first pair of words. Then find the word that *best* completes the analogy, and circle the letter in front of your word choice. Use a dictionary if you need help.

1 track : train :: highway :
 - **A.** street
 - **B.** road
 - **C.** freeway
 - **D.** truck

2 principal : school :: physician :
 - **A.** hospital
 - **B.** doctor
 - **C.** nurse
 - **D.** stethoscope

3 helicopter : sky :: canoe :
 - **A.** boat
 - **B.** paddle
 - **C.** river
 - **D.** row

4 word : dictionary :: map :
 - **A.** globe
 - **B.** atlas
 - **C.** tap
 - **D.** directions

5 suite : sweet :: thyme :
 - **A.** time
 - **B.** spice
 - **C.** rhyme
 - **D.** thigh

6 goose : geese :: ox :
 - **A.** oxs
 - **B.** oxen
 - **C.** oxes
 - **D.** mammal

7 cavern : cave :: slope :
 - **A.** dope
 - **B.** plain
 - **C.** downfall
 - **D.** incline

8 indigo : blue :: scarlet :
 - **A.** black
 - **B.** red
 - **C.** green
 - **D.** turquoise

9 century : hundred :: decade :
 - **A.** thousand
 - **B.** month
 - **C.** year
 - **D.** ten

10 renovate : restore :: question :
 - **A.** interrogate
 - **B.** ignore
 - **C.** quest
 - **D.** quarrel

Analogies and Idioms • 5–6 © 2007 Creative Teaching Press

Analogy Challenge #6

An *analogy* is the relationship between one pair of words that serves as the basis for the creation of another pair of words. In each exercise below, find the relationship between the first pair of words. Then find the word that *best* completes the analogy, and circle the letter in front of your word choice. Use a dictionary if you need help.

1 larva : larvae :: cactus :
- A. spine
- B. cactuses
- C. desert
- D. cactuss

2 birch : tree :: petunia :
- A. flower
- B. soil
- C. fruit
- D. animal

3 dwindle : shrink :: forgive :
- A. remember
- B. promise
- C. forget
- D. pardon

4 pallor : paleness :: display :
- A. dismay
- B. disapprove
- C. exhibit
- D. replay

5 sapphire : gem :: novel :
- A. book
- B. poetry
- C. title
- D. dictionary

6 quarts : quartz :: sleigh :
- A. sled
- B. reindeer
- C. slay
- D. destroy

7 obscure : distinct :: dull :
- A. hull
- B. sallow
- C. boring
- D. luminous

8 gaunt : thin :: lively :
- A. vivacious
- B. tranquil
- C. morose
- D. graceful

9 cardiologist : heart :: orthodontist :
- A. feet
- B. dentist
- C. teeth
- D. doctor

10 replica : copy :: petty :
- A. pretty
- B. trivial
- C. ready
- D. peculiar

Analogies and Idioms • 5–6 © 2007 Creative Teaching Press

Name _____ Date _____

Create Your Own Analogies

Have fun creating analogies for classmates to complete. Write six analogies using synonyms, antonyms, homophones, parts to whole, animal groups, etc. Give classmates four answers from which to choose. Be sure that the correct answer is not always in the same spot, such as choice *B* or *D*. Make an answer key to go along with your activity. Use words from the lists on page 24 as well as words from a dictionary and/or a thesaurus.

1 _____ : _____ :: _____ :

     A. _____   **C.** _____

     B. _____   **D.** _____

2 _____ : _____ :: _____ :

     A. _____   **C.** _____

     B. _____   **D.** _____

3 _____ : _____ :: _____ :

     A. _____   **C.** _____

     B. _____   **D.** _____

4 _____ : _____ :: _____ :

     A. _____   **C.** _____

     B. _____   **D.** _____

5 _____ : _____ :: _____ :

     A. _____   **C.** _____

     B. _____   **D.** _____

Create Your Own Analogies

SYNONYMS

ache / pain
aid / assist
anger / rage
apparent / obvious
area / zone
buy / purchase
clear / plain
copy / imitate
coy / shy
damp / moist
decline / refuse
depart / leave
disappear / vanish
easy / simple
empty / vacant
entire / whole
fast / quick
fierce / ferocious
foggy / misty
frequently / often
genuine / real
grief / sorrow
honest / sincere
hurry / rush
instructor / teacher
job / task
judgment / verdict
late / tardy
limp / slack
marvelous / wonderful
mend / repair
necessary / essential
opinion / view
oppose / resist
peaceful / tranquil
petty / trivial
quiver / shake
severe / harsh
useless / worthless

ANTONYMS

accept / refuse
active / passive
advance / retreat
alike / different
allow / forbid
arrive / depart
ascent / descent
attack / defend
begin / end
bold / timid
bottom / top
busy / idle
calm / excited
cheerful / somber
cold / hot
common / rare
complex / simple
cruel / kind
defense / offense
difficult / easy
dry / wet
early / late
exact / vague
fail / succeed
false / true
few / many
fresh / stale
give / take
hard / soft
high / low
inferior / superior
loose / tight
maximum / minimum
narrow / wide
often / seldom
permanent / temporary
save / spend
shrink / swell
sick / healthy
thick / thin
wild / tame

HOMOPHONES

aisle / isle
ant / aunt
bail / bale
bare / bear
beat / beet
billed / build
boar / bore
bread / bred
bridal / bridle
capital / capitol
cellar / seller
chute / shoot
close / clothes
coarse / course
creak / creek
doe / dough
fair / fare
feat / feet
genes / jeans
grate / great
hair / hare
higher / hire
hoarse / horse
hole / whole
knead / need
knight / night
loan / lone
moan / mown
naval / navel
one / won
peak / peek
pedal / peddle
principal / principle
quarts / quartz
raise / rays
scene / seen
straight / strait
team / teem
throne / thrown
waist / waste
wood / would

Analogies and Idioms • 5–6 © 2007 Creative Teaching Press

What Is an Idiom?

An *idiom* is the assigning of a new meaning to a group of words each of which already has its own meaning.

Here are some examples of some common idioms:

Spill the beans does not mean that someone has poured beans onto the table or floor. It means to tell a secret to someone who is not supposed to know about it. Here is the idiom used in a sentence.

"I almost *spilled the beans* and told her about the gift he got her for her birthday," said Sarah.

All thumbs does not mean a person only has thumbs on his or her hand. It means that a person is very clumsy. Here is the idiom used in a sentence.

"I am *all thumbs* when it comes to sewing. I can't even sew a button on a shirt," said Yolanda.

Idiom Practice

Select the best meaning for the words in italics to show you understand the meaning of each idiom.

1 If a project in a lab is *under wraps*, it is
- **A.** covered with plastic.
- **B.** being kept hidden or secret.
- **C.** decorated with ribbons and paper.
- **D.** being revised or expanded.

2 If someone *does a double take*, he or she
- **A.** repeats a play in baseball.
- **B.** sings a duet.
- **C.** purchases two of the exact same product in a store.
- **D.** looks again in surprise.

3 If someone does something *with bells on*, he or she does it
- **A.** with enthusiasm.
- **B.** accompanied by a lot of noise.
- **C.** with doubt or confusion.
- **D.** with fear.

4 If a student *burns the midnight oil*, he or she
- **A.** lights a fire to stay warm on a cold night.
- **B.** does several tasks at the same time.
- **C.** stays up late at night to study.
- **D.** drives a car late at night.

Analogies and Idioms • 5–6 © 2007 Creative Teaching Press

Make My Day

Match each idiom with its meaning by writing the correct letter on the line.

1 _____ make oneself scarce

2 _____ make way

3 _____ make a beeline for

4 _____ make a go of

5 _____ make a mountain out of a molehill

6 _____ make eyes at

7 _____ make no bones

8 _____ make one's blood boil

9 _____ make ends meet

10 _____ make one's mouth water

A. to think a small problem is a big one

B. to cause to be a success

C. to stand aside

D. to have no doubts; to make no secret

E. to have enough money to pay one's bills

F. to go in a straight line towards

G. to make someone very angry

H. to look or smell very good

I. to go away; to leave quickly

J. to flirt

Analogies and Idioms • 5–6 © 2007 Creative Teaching Press

Right On

Match each idiom with its meaning by writing the correct letter on the line.

1 _____ on the block

2 _____ on the spur of the moment

3 _____ on the blink

4 _____ on the mend

5 _____ on the up and up

6 _____ on the ball

7 _____ on the house

8 _____ on the sly

9 _____ on the dot

10 _____ on hand

A. honest; trustworthy

B. secretly

C. doing things well

D. nearby; within reach

E. paid for by the owner

F. suddenly; without thought
   or preparation

G. for sale; to be sold

H. needing repair; not working well

I. exactly on time

J. healing

Let's Have It

Match each idiom with its meaning by writing the correct letter on the line.

1 _____ let off steam

2 _____ let on

3 _____ let sleeping dogs lie

4 _____ let up

5 _____ let grass grow under one's feet

6 _____ let the cat out of the bag

7 _____ let bygones be bygones

8 _____ let down easy

9 _____ let it all hang out

10 _____ let ride

A. to become weaker or less; becoming slower

B. to tell bad news about a disappointment in a kindly way

C. to get rid of physical energy or strong feelings through activity

D. to tell about something that is supposed to be a secret

E. to allow to go on without change; accept for the present

F. to not make someone angry and cause danger or trouble

G. to let the past be forgotten

H. to let the truth be known

I. to tell or admit what one knows

J. to be lazy; to waste time

Do You Get It?

Match each idiom with its meaning by writing the correct letter on the line.

1 _____ get a word in edgewise

2 _____ get the ax

3 _____ get through one's head

4 _____ get with it

5 _____ get wind of

6 _____ get under one's skin

7 _____ get one's feet wet

8 _____ get up on the wrong side of the bed

9 _____ get off one's back

10 _____ get a load of

A. to find out about; hear rumors about

B. to find a chance to say something when other people are talking

C. to pay attention; get busy

D. to awaken with a bad temper or in a bad mood

E. to be fired from a job

F. to stop nagging or criticizing someone

G. to upset or bother

H. to take a good look at

I. to do something for the first time; to begin

J. to understand or believe

Take a Look

Match each idiom with its meaning by writing the correct letter on the line.

1 _____ take for granted

2 _____ take exception to

3 _____ take in stride

4 _____ take a back seat

5 _____ take off one's hat to

6 _____ take its toll

7 _____ take to the woods

8 _____ take the bull by the horns

9 _____ take the words out of one's mouth

10 _____ take it easy

A. to find fault with; to speak against

B. to accept good or bad luck and continue on

C. to run away and hide

D. to accept a lower position; be second to something

E. to take action and not care about the risks

F. to cause loss or damage

G. to act or go carefully or slowly

H. to understand to be true

I. to praise or respect someone

J. to say what someone else was just going to say

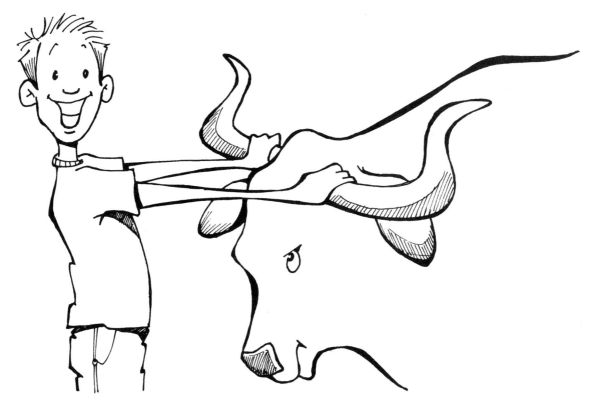

Analogies and Idioms • 5–6 © 2007 Creative Teaching Press

Name _____ Date _____

What's Up?

Match each idiom with its meaning by writing the correct letter on the line.

1 _____ up the creek without a paddle

2 _____ up for grabs

3 _____ up one's sleeve

4 _____ up front

5 _____ up to par

6 _____ up in arms

7 _____ up in the air

8 _____ up against

9 _____ upper crust

10 _____ upper hand

A. sincere; open; not hiding anything

B. unsettled; undecided; uncertain

C. the highest class; the most famous or richest

D. up to the usual level or quality

E. having trouble or difficulty and being unable to do anything about it

F. advantage; controlling power

G. available for anyone to try and get; there for the taking

H. angry and ready to fight

I. blocked or threatened by

J. kept secretly ready for the right time when needed

Analogies and Idioms • 5–6 © 2007 Creative Teaching Press

Pull It Off

Match each idiom with its meaning by writing the correct letter on the line.

1 _____ pull out of a hat

2 _____ pull the rug out from under

3 _____ pull rank

4 _____ pull one's weight

5 _____ pull over

6 _____ pull off

7 _____ pull strings

8 _____ pull the wool over one's eyes

9 _____ pull the plug on

10 _____ pull through

A. to unexpectedly withdraw support from; to spoil someone's plans

B. to invent; imagine; to get as if by magic

C. to make use of friends or people in authority to gain one's wishes

D. to assert one's authority on a person of lower rank

E. to recover from an illness or misfortune; save

F. to do one's part; to do one's full share of work

G. to stop one's support of something

H. to succeed or do

I. to deceive

J. to drive to the side of the road and come to a stop

Analogies and Idioms • 5–6 © 2007 Creative Teaching Press

Come Along

Match each idiom with its meaning by writing the correct letter on the line.

1 _____ come a long way

2 _____ come clean

3 _____ come full circle

4 _____ come to blows

5 _____ come to terms

6 _____ come down with

7 _____ come in handy

8 _____ come into one's own

9 _____ come off it

10 _____ come on strong

A. to change and develop, only to end up in the same place one started

B. to catch or to become sick with

C. to make great progress

D. to receive the respect, recognition, or prosperity one deserves

E. to begin to fight

F. to stop being silly; stop pretending or kidding

G. to reach an understanding or agreement

H. to insist extremely strongly

I. to confess; to tell the whole story

J. to prove useful

Analogies and Idioms • 5–6 © 2007 Creative Teaching Press

Keep It Going

Match each idiom with its meaning by writing the correct letter on the line.

1 _____ keep one's head

2 _____ keep under one's hat

3 _____ keep one's eye on the ball

4 _____ keep one's nose clean

5 _____ keep tabs on

6 _____ keep up with the Joneses

7 _____ keep one's chin up

8 _____ keep after

9 _____ keep one's shirt on

10 _____ keep the ball rolling

A. to stay out of trouble

B. to be brave; to face trouble with courage

C. to be watchful and ready; to be smart

D. to stay calm in time of trouble or danger

E. to compete with one's neighbors

F. to keep up an activity or action

G. to calm down; keep from getting excited or impatient

H. to not tell; to keep secret

I. to check; to keep a record of

J. to remind someone over and over again

Analogies and Idioms • 5–6 © 2007 Creative Teaching Press

In the Works

Match each idiom with its meaning by writing the correct letter on the line.

1 _____ in a fog

2 _____ in the bag

3 _____ in the doghouse

4 _____ in the works

5 _____ in vain

6 _____ in the same boat

7 _____ in the dark

8 _____ in the clear

9 _____ in stitches

10 _____ in nothing flat

A. certain; sure to be won or gotten

B. in progress; being worked on or planned

C. in a fit of laughing hard

D. in the same bad situation

E. in trouble; in disfavor or disgrace

F. soon; quickly

G. without success

H. free of blame or suspicion

I. without information; in ignorance

J. confused; not sure what is happening

Have a Go at It

Match each idiom with its meaning by writing the correct letter on the line.

1 _____ have one's hands full

2 _____ have it made

3 _____ have rocks in one's head

4 _____ have it out

5 _____ have a ball

6 _____ have a go at

7 _____ have an edge on

8 _____ have a screw loose

9 _____ have an eye for

10 _____ have a time

A. to have good taste in; to be able to judge correctly

B. to have an advantage over someone else

C. to have a great time; to enjoy oneself

D. to settle a difference by a fight or by a discussion

E. to act in a strange way; to be foolish

F. to be stupid; to not have good judgment

G. to try, especially after other people have tried

H. to be very busy

I. to have trouble; to have a hard time

J. to be certain of success; to have everything one needs

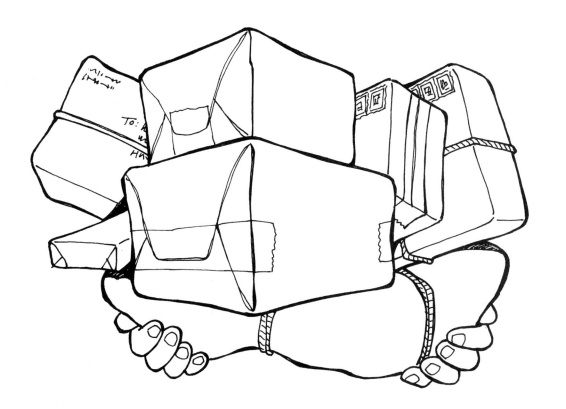

Analogies and Idioms • 5–6 © 2007 Creative Teaching Press

Turn the Tables

Match each idiom with its meaning by writing the correct letter on the line.

1. _____ turn over a new leaf
2. _____ turn thumbs down
3. _____ turn the clock back
4. _____ turn one's back on
5. _____ turn on one's heels
6. _____ turn a deaf ear
7. _____ turn the tide
8. _____ turn one's stomach
9. _____ turn up one's nose at
10. _____ turn to jelly

A. to refuse to help someone in need or trouble

B. to not pay attention; to pretend not to hear

C. to make a sudden change for the better in behavior

D. to make you feel sick

E. to change what looks like defeat into victory

F. to return to an earlier period

G. to refuse as not being good enough for you

H. to turn around very suddenly

I. to become shaky because of fear or exhaustion

J. to say no; to reject or disapprove

Analogies and Idioms • 5–6 © 2007 Creative Teaching Press

Name _____ Date _____

At Last!

Match each idiom with its meaning by writing the correct letter on the line.

1 _____ at one's fingertips

2 _____ at the drop of a hat

3 _____ at one's heels

4 _____ at the top of one's lungs

5 _____ at this rate

6 _____ at times

7 _____ at the tip of one's tongue

8 _____ at first glance

9 _____ at odds

10 _____ at length

A. very loudly; as loud as one can

B. within easy reach; nearby

C. almost spoken or remembered

D. promptly; immediately

E. after a first quick look

F. fully; in detail

G. not often; not every day

H. close behind

I. opposed; in disagreement

J. at a speed like this

Analogies and Idioms • 5–6 © 2007 Creative Teaching Press

Go to Town

Match each idiom with its meaning by writing the correct letter on the line.

1 _____ go haywire

2 _____ go for broke

3 _____ go over like a lead balloon

4 _____ go up in smoke

5 _____ go back on

6 _____ go on

7 _____ go out of one's way

8 _____ go to town

9 _____ go overboard

10 _____ go to one's head

A. to meet with boredom or disapproval; to fail to generate enthusiasm

B. to go out of order; be damaged

C. to turn against; to fail to honor or keep

D. to make a person think he or she is too important

E. to try as hard as possible

F. to act excitedly and without careful thinking

G. to work hard or fast; succeed

H. disappear; not come true; to burn

I. to do more than usual; to make an extra effort

J. to continue; not stop

Lay Eyes on This

Match each idiom with its meaning by writing the correct letter on the line.

1 _____ lay down the law

2 _____ lay over

3 _____ lay to rest

4 _____ lay a finger on

5 _____ lay eyes on

6 _____ lay into

7 _____ lay it on thick

8 _____ lay low

9 _____ lay one's cards on the table

10 _____ lay one's hands on

A. to see

B. to hide; to stay out of sight

C. to flatter

D. to deal honestly; to act without secrets or trickery

E. to give strict orders

F. to attack verbally or physically

G. to arrive in one place and wait some time before continuing the journey

H. to bury; stop

I. to get possession of

J. to touch or bother

Analogies and Idioms • 5–6 © 2007 Creative Teaching Press

Name _____ Date _____

Under the Weather

Match each idiom with its meaning by writing the correct letter on the line.

1 _____ under one's nose

2 _____ under a cloud

3 _____ under one's wing

4 _____ under one's belt

5 _____ under one's thumb

6 _____ under the circumstances

7 _____ under the weather

8 _____ under one's breath

9 _____ under fire

10 _____ under one's own steam

A. under someone's power or control

B. under the care or protection of

C. in sight of; easily seen or noticed

D. without help; by one's own effort

E. depressed; sad; discouraged

F. feeling slightly sick or ill

G. in the present condition; as things are

H. in a low voice or whisper

I. in a person's experience, memory, or possession

J. under attack; being shot at

Analogies and Idioms • 5–6 © 2007 Creative Teaching Press

Name _____ Date _____

Off the Top of Your Head

Match each idiom with its meaning by writing the correct letter on the line.

1 _____ off the hook

2 _____ off guard

3 _____ off one's rocker

4 _____ off the beam

5 _____ off the top of one's head

6 _____ off one's chest

7 _____ off the cuff

8 _____ off one's hands

9 _____ off and on

10 _____ off duty

A. without thinking hard; quickly

B. out of trouble

C. wrong; mistaken

D. told to someone and so not bothering a person any more

E. no longer in one's care or possession

F. not alert to the unexpected

G. not working

H. without preparation

I. occasionally; not regularly

J. crazy; foolish

Analogies and Idioms • 5–6 © 2007 Creative Teaching Press

Name _____ Date _____

Match a Missing Word

Find the word that completes each idiom. Write the missing words on the lines.

1 climbing the _____

2 foaming at the _____

3 burning the candle at both _____

4 raining cats and _____

5 pulling one's own _____

6 crying over spilled _____

7 going around in _____

8 getting away with _____

9 barking up the wrong _____

10 flying off the _____

A. dogs

B. circles

C. tree

D. milk

E. handle

F. ends

G. weight

H. murder

I. mouth

J. wall

Name _____ Date _____

What Do You Do?

Select the best meaning for the words in italics to show you understand the meaning of each idiom.

1 What do you do when you *tie the knot*?
- **A.** get dressed
- **B.** get married
- **C.** get in trouble
- **D.** get something to eat

2 What do you do when you *spill the beans*?
- **A.** make a mistake
- **B.** burn the vegetables
- **C.** laugh out loud
- **D.** disclose a secret

3 What do you do when you *come clean*?
- **A.** confess; tell the whole story
- **B.** go in the ocean
- **C.** take a shower
- **D.** wash the car

4 What do you do when you *skate on thin ice*?
- **A.** skate in an ice rink
- **B.** take a chance or risk danger
- **C.** have fun with friends
- **D.** force someone to do something against his/her wishes

5 What do you do when you *call it a day*?
- **A.** tell what day of the week it is
- **B.** check the calendar
- **C.** quit
- **D.** arrive

6 What do you do when you *kill two birds with one stone*?
- **A.** shoot two birds sitting together on a wire
- **B.** eat twice as much as you usually do
- **C.** get even with someone
- **D.** succeed in doing two things by only one action

7 What do you do when you *burn up the road*?
- **A.** spend too much money on an item
- **B.** purchase new tires for a car or truck
- **C.** drive a car very fast
- **D.** make a fire in the middle of the road

Analogies and Idioms • 5–6 © 2007 Creative Teaching Press

Pick a Person

Match each idiom with its meaning by writing the correct letter on the line.

1 _____ a knockout

2 _____ a chip off the old block

3 _____ a man in the street

4 _____ a sitting duck

5 _____ an oddball

6 _____ a dark horse

7 _____ a runner

8 _____ a jack of all trades

9 _____ a pip-squeak

10 _____ a fair-weather friend

A. a small, unimportant person

B. someone who is knowledgeable in many areas

C. an unsuspecting or naïve person who is easily fooled

D. one who doesn't act like everyone else

E. a person who acts or looks like one of his parents

F. a beautiful woman

G. one who performs messenger services

H. an average or ordinary person

I. a person or team not expected to win

J. a person who is a friend in good times but is not a friend in times of trouble

Analogies and Idioms • 5–6 © 2007 Creative Teaching Press

Answer Key

Synonym Analogies (page 5)

1. C
2. B
3. D
4. B
5. C
6. D
7. C
8. D
9. B
10. C

More Synonym Analogies (page 6)

1. B
2. C
3. A
4. D
5. B
6. C
7. B
8. D
9. B
10. A

Antonym Analogies (page 7)

1. C
2. B
3. C
4. A
5. C
6. D
7. C
8. B
9. A
10. C

Synonym and Antonym Analogies (page 8)

1. D
2. A
3. C
4. B
5. C
6. A
7. C
8. B
9. B
10. C

Noun Analogies (page 9)

1. B
2. C
3. D
4. C
5. D
6. A
7. A
8. D
9. B
10. C

Verb Analogies (page 10)

1. C
2. A
3. B
4. D
5. B
6. A
7. C
8. B
9. C
10. D

Adjective Analogies (page 11)

1. D
2. A
3. B
4. D
5. B
6. C
7. A
8. D
9. C
10. B

Adverb Analogies (page 12)

1. B
2. D
3. B
4. D
5. A
6. C
7. D
8. C
9. B
10. A

Food Analogies (page 13)

1. A
2. C
3. B
4. D
5. A
6. B
7. D
8. A
9. C
10. D

Sports Analogies (page 14)

1. C
2. D
3. A
4. C
5. C
6. D
7. B
8. A
9. B
10. A

Number and Measurement Analogies (page 15)

1. B
2. C
3. D
4. B
5. C
6. A
7. B
8. A
9. C
10. D

Animal Analogies (page 16)

1. A
2. C
3. D
4. D
5. B
6. C
7. A
8. D
9. D
10. B

Analogy Challenge #1 (page 17)

1. B
2. D
3. A
4. D
5. B
6. A
7. C
8. D
9. D
10. C

Analogy Challenge #2 (page 18)

1. C
2. A
3. D
4. B
5. A
6. C
7. D
8. B
9. A
10. C

Analogy Challenge #3 (page 19)

1. D
2. A
3. B
4. D
5. D
6. C
7. B
8. A
9. B
10. C

Analogy Challenge #4 (page 20)

1. B
2. D
3. D
4. C
5. A
6. D
7. A
8. D
9. C
10. A

Analogy Challenge #5 (page 21)

1. D
2. A
3. C
4. B
5. A
6. B
7. D
8. B
9. D
10. A

Analogy Challenge #6 (page 22)

1. B
2. A
3. D
4. C
5. A
6. C
7. D
8. A
9. C
10. B

What Is an Idiom? (page 25)

1. B
2. D
3. A
4. C

Make My Day (page 26)

1. I
2. C
3. F
4. B
5. A
6. J
7. D
8. G
9. E
10. H

Right On (page 27)

1. G
2. F
3. H
4. J
5. A
6. C
7. E
8. B
9. I
10. D

Let's Have It (page 28)

1. C
2. I
3. F
4. A
5. J
6. D
7. G
8. B
9. H
10. E

Do You Get It? (page 29)

1. B
2. E
3. J
4. C
5. A
6. G
7. I
8. D
9. F
10. H

Take a Look (page 30)

1. H
2. A
3. B
4. D
5. I
6. F
7. C
8. E
9. J
10. G

What's Up? (page 31)

1. E
2. G
3. J
4. A
5. D
6. H
7. B
8. I
9. C
10. F

Pull It Off (page 32)

1. B
2. A
3. D
4. F
5. J
6. H
7. C
8. I
9. G
10. E

Come Along (page 33)

1. C
2. I
3. A
4. E
5. G
6. B
7. J
8. D
9. F
10. H

Keep It Going (page 34)

1. D
2. H
3. C
4. A
5. I
6. E
7. B
8. J
9. G
10. F

In the Works (page 35)

1. J
2. A
3. E
4. B
5. G
6. D
7. I
8. H
9. C
10. F

Have a Go at It (page 36)

1. H
2. J
3. F
4. D
5. C
6. G
7. B
8. E
9. A
10. I

Turn the Tables (page 37)

1. C
2. J
3. F
4. A
5. H
6. B
7. E
8. D
9. G
10. I

At Last! (page 38)

1. B
2. D
3. H
4. A
5. J
6. G
7. C
8. E
9. I
10. F

Go to Town (page 39)

1. B
2. E
3. A
4. H
5. C
6. J
7. I
8. G
9. F
10. D

Lay Eyes on This (page 40)

1. E
2. G
3. H
4. J
5. A
6. F
7. C
8. B
9. D
10. I

Under the Weather (page 41)

1. C
2. E
3. B
4. I
5. A
6. G
7. F
8. H
9. J
10. D

Off the Top of Your Head (page 42)

1. B
2. F
3. J
4. C
5. A
6. D
7. H
8. E
9. I
10. G

Match a Missing Word (page 43)

1. J. wall
2. I. mouth
3. F. ends
4. A. dogs
5. G. weight
6. D. milk
7. B. circles
8. H. murder
9. C. tree
10. E. handle

What Do You Do? (page 44)

1. B
2. D
3. A
4. B
5. C
6. D
7. C

Pick a Person (page 45)

1. F
2. E
3. H
4. C
5. D
6. I
7. G
8. B
9. A
10. J